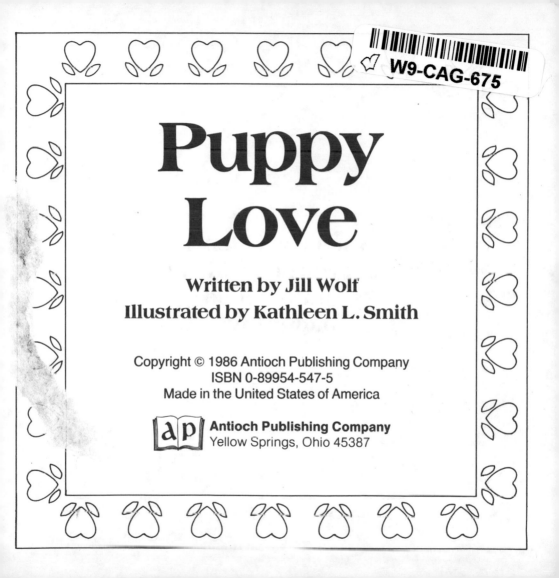

Puppy Love

Written by Jill Wolf
Illustrated by Kathleen L. Smith

Copyright © 1986 Antioch Publishing Company
ISBN 0-89954-547-5
Made in the United States of America

Antioch Publishing Company
Yellow Springs, Ohio 45387

When you're lonely
and you find a friend,
you've found
puppy love.

**Puppy love is wondering
whether a certain someone
<u>really</u> likes you or not.**

**With puppy love,
even a rainy day
seems less lonely.**

If you always seem
to end up together,
you're in
puppy love.

When you're sleepy or sad,
puppy love gives you
a shoulder to
lay your head on.

**The fun of puppy love
is discovering
new things together.**

**Puppy love
is understanding
when someone feels
hurt or sad.**

**Liking someone
very different from you
proves it's more
than puppy love.**

**Puppy love means
sharing everything—
especially the blame
when you get into trouble.**

**Giving each other
little presents
is part of
puppy love.**

Puppy love is the warm and happy feeling of your very first kiss.

The End